Dot's Big Red Hat

by Liza Charlesworth

ISBN: 978-1-338-84429-0

Art Director: Tannaz Fassihi; Designer: Cynthia Ng; Illustrated by Kevin Zimmer
Copyright © Liza Charlesworth. All rights reserved. Published by Scholastic Inc.

3 4 5 6 7 68 26 25 24

Printed in Jiaxing, China. First printing, June 2022.

SCHOLASTIC

Dot had a big red hat.
Dot set it on top
of a box.

"DAB-DIB-A-DUB!" said Dot.
The hat had a mug in it!

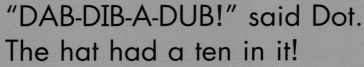

"DAB-DIB-A-DUB!" said Dot.
The hat had a ten in it!

4

"DAB-DIB-A-DUB!" said Dot.
The hat had a sub in it!

"DAB-DIB-A-DUB!" said Dot.
The hat had a can in it!

"DAB-DIB-A-DUB!" said Dot.
The hat had a pup in it!

"Yap, yap!" said the pup.
"The pup is my pet!" said Dot.
Dot fed him a lot.

"DAB-DIB-A-DUB!" said Dot.
The hat had a bag in it!

Dot put the mug, ten, and sub in the bag.

"DAB-DIB-A-DUB!" said Dot.
The hat had a cab in it!

"DAB-DIB-A-DUB!" said Dot.
The cab got BIG, BIG, BIG!

Dot got in the cab
with the bag and pet.
"Yap, yap!" said the pup.

Read & Review

Invite your learner to point to each short-vowel word and read it aloud.

Short a

yap   bag

cab   and

dab   can

had   hat

Short e

ten   red
set
pet
fed

Short o

top   on
       Dot   got
box
       lot

Short i

is big   it
kid him
dib   in

Short u

pup
       mug
dub
   sub

15

Fun Fill-Ins

Read the sentences aloud, inviting your learner to complete them using the short-vowel words in the box.

> hat   Dot   big   pup   ten

1. This story was about a girl named _____.
2. Dot had a big red _____.
3. In the hat was a number _____.
4. "Yap, yap!" said the _____.
5. The cab got big, big, _____!